Your partner in education

**Distributed by Grolier, Sherman Turnpike
Danbury, Connecticut 06816**

Grolier offers a varied selection of
children's book racks and tote bags.
For details on ordering, please write:
Grolier Direct Marketing
Sherman Turnpike
Danbury, CT 06816
Att: Premium Department

My a Book

by Jane Belk Moncure
illustrated by Pam Peltier

THE CHILD'S WORLD

Mankato, MN 56001

Little a had a box.

He said, "I will fill my  box ."

Little a put on his hat and went for a walk.

He found
apples,
apples,
apples.

He put the apples into his box.

Little  found an alligator.

He put the alligator into his box.

Little  found ants,
ants, ants.

"In you go, ants," he said.

Then Little  found arrows,
arrows,
arrows.

Did he put the arrows into
his box?

box

He did!

Little a found an ax.

It was a toy ax.

He put the ax into the box.

Now the box was so full …

the ants,

the arrows,

and the ax
fell out.

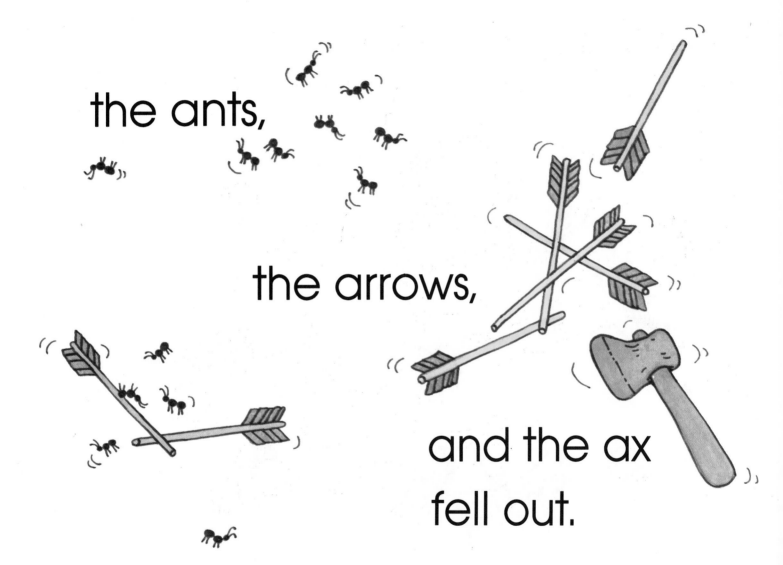

The apples and
the alligator

fell out too.

"Who will help me
fill my box?" said Little .

An astronaut came by.
"I will help you," said the astronaut.

"We will fill your box."

Then the astronaut

took Little  for a ride.

Up, up, and away!

ants

alligator

arrows

astronaut

apples

ax

27

More words with Little

antelope

acrobat

antlers

anchor

animals

ambulance

Little  has another sound in some words.

He says his name.
Listen for Little 's name.

acorn

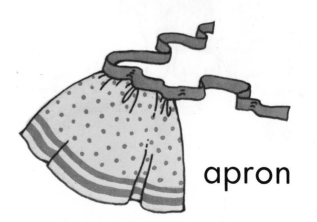

apron